Dear Alex and Zoe,

We hope you enjoy reading these poems about Canadian ani[mals].

We miss and love you!

Aunt Mary Beth
Uncle Malcolm

7/19

A Canadian 🍁 Wildlife Poem

This book is dedicated to my parents Joyce and Ray Elliott, who always got their children outside to play, and to my best friend Greg Dineen, who still gets me outside to play!

A CANADIAN WILDLIFE POEM
Published by Max Elliott
PO Box 2344 . Banff AB . T1L 1C1 . Canada
maxelliottbooks@gmail.com

1st edition – 2014

Design: Linda Petras
Photography: John Bonner
Printed in Canada by Friesens

Library and Archives Canada Cataloguing in Publication

Elliott, Max, 1962-, author
     A Canadian wildlife poem / words and pictures by Max Elliott.

ISBN 978-0-9937228-0-6 (bound)
     1. Animals—Canada—Juvenile poetry. I. Title.

PS8609.L5497C35 2014   jC811'.6   C2014-904814-9

A Canadian Wildlife Poem

by Max Elliott

The polar bear has an
oily fur coat
to keep it toasty warm

With its layer of blubber,
a harbour seal
can weather any storm

A beaver will warn with a *slap* of its tail
if it feels that danger is near

And a flash of white
    is warning enough
        if you're a white-tailed deer

The enormous size
of a killer whale
might give it little to fear

But being small
can top it all
when a wood frog wants
to disappear

A fierce and fearless wolverine
has claws to climb and dig

The musk ox proves
  you can dig with hooves,
    and it's faster if they're big!

For climbing craft,
the mountain goat
will leave the rest behind

Swimming uphill is the salmon's skill,
and one you'll rarely find

On the tundra, caribou
trek on hooves splayed wide

The lynx has paws that,
snowshoe like,
improve its winter stride

The fox relies on cleverness
to keep it out of trouble

Its markings hide
this ptarmigan
amidst the hillside rubble

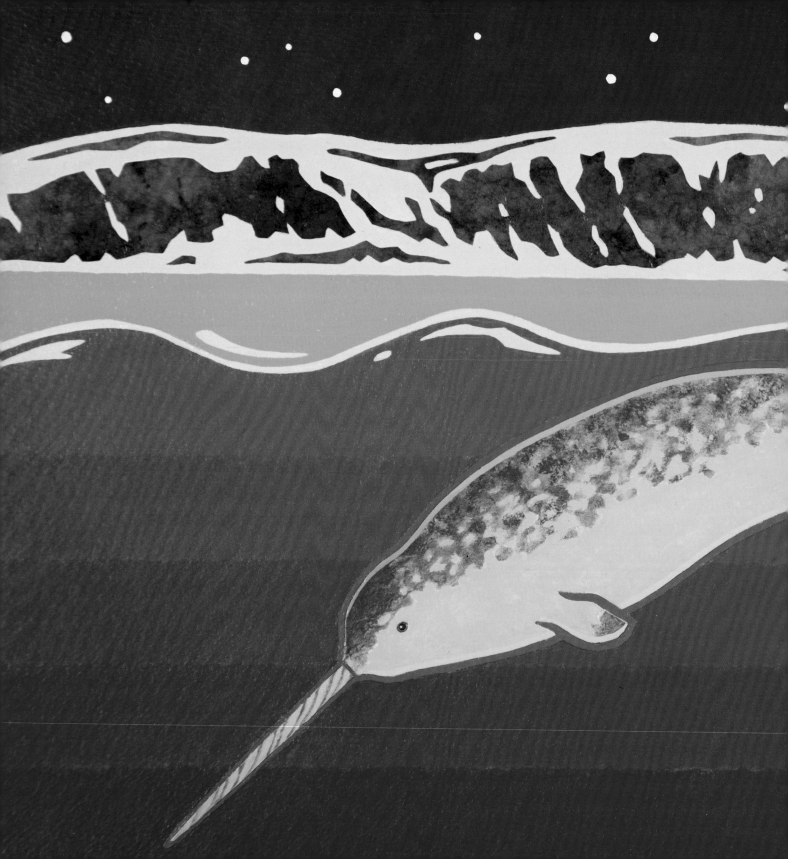

In Arctic waters
   a narwhal dives
      into the icy deep

While high above, a snowy owl
   goes hunting while we sleep

A cougar sees its prey then,
silent,
holds its body still

The Atlantic puffin
carries fish
crosswise in its bill

Raccoons will look for
food in streams,
dabbling as they search

Porcupines may browse
on branches from a
treetop perch

Bison make their homes in woods
or on a golden plain

A walrus, though,
as you may know,
likes ocean-side terrain

Squirrels chatter,
busy storing food for their survival

Canada geese
honk loudly
to announce their
spring arrival

Loons will mate,
one pair per pond,
and enchant us with their call

An Arctic wolf pack
works together
to care for one and all

Baby moose will skip and splash,
and embrace any reason to play

And grizzly bears,
   in the comfort of caves,
      can sleep a whole season away!